The Luck of TWO DUCKS

A True Story

JESSE ACKERMAN

PAGE PUBLISHING
Conneaut Lake, PA

First originally published by Page Publishing 2023

ISBN 979-8-89157-438-0 (pbk)
ISBN 979-8-89157-455-7 (digital)

Printed in the United States of America

Christine,

Thanks for always lifting us up
and being our rock.

DC,

You are the best of us. We are blessed and
truly the luckiest ducks with you in our life.

Love,
Dad

In memoriam
of Clive Brown

Denny and Curt were two of the same.

They would paddle and play in their pond all day.

In good weather or bad, when times were tough or the other was sad.

These two ducks stayed side by side and worked together so they could thrive.

4

Denny and Curt were the best of
friends, and everyone could see.

5

Even though they were a little different like all ducks tend to be.

6

Denny had freckles all over his webbed feet, whereas Curt's were bigger and orange colors ran deep.

Curt and Denny waddled around like ducks do. The size and look did not matter, both still worked the way feet do.

Curt's chest was big, but Denny's was not.

However, both kept them afloat when they paddled along the water top.

Denny's wings were long when he spread them way out wide.

Curt's were a little shorter, but he
could still fly very, very high.

Curt's bill was yellow, with a bunch of small freckles. Denny's was orange, with barely a speckle.

13

QUACK!
QUACK!
QUACK!

Both would quack and make sounds familiar to you. They would even make songs that you could dance to too.

14

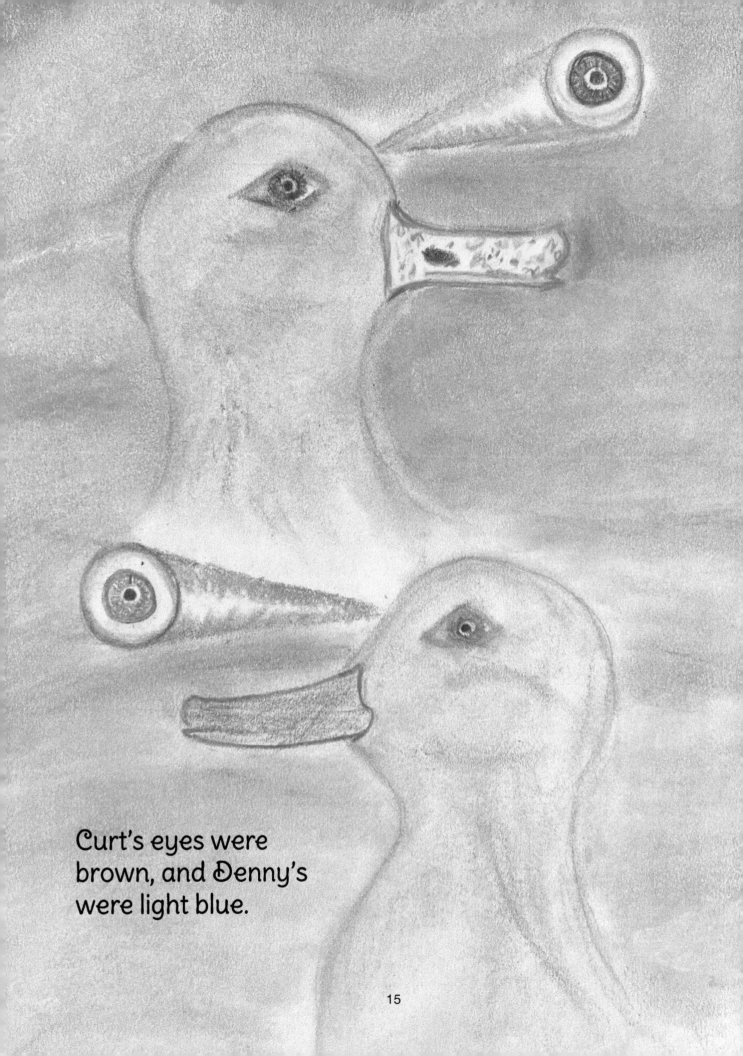

Curt's eyes were
brown, and Denny's
were light blue.

15

Both could see clearly even
though they look different to you.

Their feathers were beautiful and would glisten in the sun. Some looked very different. Can you tell which ones?

Along with the shape and how their feathers were arranged, one more thing was different as you'll see on the next page.

Denny's feathers were white,
with some shades of gray.

Curt's feathers were black and beautiful all the same.

Curt could be quiet at times and had some very deep thoughts, whereas Denny liked to draw and could talk, talk, *talk*.

Both quacked, paddled, and sometimes flew to get away.

Their bills and feet were similar and used in the same way.

22

KIND FUN
BRAVE GOOFY
CREATIVE LOYAL
SILLY GIVING
SMART CARING

Denny and Curt were different in some ways you could view, but little things never got in the way of their friendship, which was true.

You see, the luck of two ducks was the way they saw each other inside.

FUN HAPPY
STRONG
SILLY GIVING
TRUE
KIND CARING
BOLD SMART

They did not judge each other by the color of their feathers or the color of their eyes.

Denny and Curt still live on a pond far, far away, and the spirit they showed can live inside of us today.

It's never too late to live by one simple rule: treat others as you would like others to treat you. And remember...

Ducks of a different-colored feather can be friends and can still flock together.

The Ducks

Curtis Jones, Jr.

Dennis R Ackerman

About the Author

Jesse Ackerman was born and raised in northeast Ohio, where the importance of family and work ethic are instilled at a very young age. It's no wonder he fell in love with sports and physical culture growing up in an environment that encourages passion for competition, but equally emphasizes the importance of detailed work. This led to success on the football field as a player and to a career in coaching that has spanned over twenty years.

As a strength and conditioning coach, he's worked in collegiate, professional, tactical, and private settings.

His professional career includes a Super Bowl and BCS National Championship appearance with numerous Bowl game appearances. Jesse has worked with future NFL Hall of Famers, elite special operations soldiers, and elite-level collegiate student-athletes from various sports. He is grateful for the opportunities he's had to work with so many high performers as they have taught him far more than he has taught them.

Jesse currently resides in Winter Garden, Florida, with his beautiful wife, Christine, and son, DC. He loves spending time with his family, cooking, sketching, and chasing DC around. Jesse lives by the motto "Love the process" and is lifelong learner that loves helping others achieve great things. He and his wife offer in-person and virtual consulting and training services at ackermanperformance.com.